For Mom, Dad, Ryan, Becca, Patrick, Justin, Grandma, and the girls who broke my heart.

(Except you, Susan.)

CRESTWELL BOOKS

— Publishers since 1922 —

crestwellbooks.com

Library of Congress Cataloging-in-Publication Data

Names: Stimmel, Grant, author.
Title: "F" is for Flush / Grant Stimmel
Description: Charlotte, N.C. : Crestwell Books, 2021
Identifiers: ISBN 978-1-7374666-0-4 (paperback)
Subjects: FICTION / Literary.

Printed in the United States of America (or somewhere in southeast Asia)
67 54 55 43 52 58 61 60 63 49 58 66 73 45 47

"Each of our stories pivot on a single moment.
That short pause between what is and what could be.
In a breath, we can decide between what we wish to be true...
and what we can make happen."

-Maaza Mengiste

"oh nein! it's raining on my schitzel!"

THE YEAR IS 2273.

Scholars looking for priceless Beanie Babies excavate a marshy outcropping near the now coastal city of Omaha, Nebraska.

They discover something that will shake them to their very core.

Deep within the mud lies a book.

THIS book.

With slow, quivering fingers...

They cautiously turn to the first page.

This is what they see.

AN ELEPHANT'S BUTTHOLE?

Oh my.

Yes.

They look each other in the eye.

"Could it really be?" they wonder.

"Is *this* the sacred text?"

With racing hearts, they brush off the front cover to reveal just 4 words:

"F" IS FOR FLUSH.

THE YEAR IS NOW.

You hold in your hands something very special.

Perhaps the key to life itself.

The world's WORST book.

Others have tried — *Twilight, The Scarlet Letter, The Story of my Life by Grant Stimmel*

But NO ONE has produced a tale quite this bad.

THINGS TO KNOW.

I didn't illustrate this book.*

YOU did.

Specifically, 102 Kickstarter backers.

And let me tell you something...

Y'all are pretty messed up.

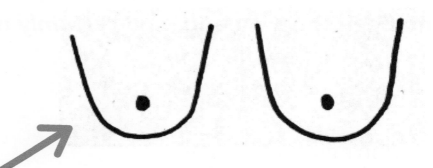

(*My uncle, uh, I mean my *lawyer* says that statement should fend off any lawsuits.)

THINGS TO KNOW.

This book has 550 words with one-of-a-kind definitions.

It has no beginning, no end, and *certainly* no plot.

Read it sporadically, or all at once.

(Frankly, I don't give a sh*t.)

And if you ever find yourself thinking, "Huh, this book kinda sucks..."

It's literally a book designed to be read while you poop.

What did you expect?!

THINGS TO KNOW.

If you're easily offended, put down this book.

(It's RIDDLED with crudely drawn penises.)

If, however, you have far too much time on your hands...

Buckle up.

It's showtime, baby.

Aunt — like your mom, but worse.

Bacon — the ONLY acceptable breakfast side. (I'm looking at you, sausage links.)

Cab — Uber for old people.

Dentures — somebody pass the corn on the cob.

Emissions — this '93 Accord is a hybrid.

Furious — when just being mad simply won't do.

Glue — like tape, but far, far more likely to be ingested.

Hum — a surefire way to annoy everyone around you.

Italy — like Uzbekistan, or so I'm told.

July — the month every mosquito in the world is born, apparently.

Kansas — EASILY the 43rd best state.

Lemonade — 75% of an 8-year-old's GDP.

Mood — generally terrible, sometimes OK.

Nanny — these snot-nosed kids won't raise themselves.

Ouch — stubbing your toe while you have a brain freeze.

Pigs — really got the short end of the stick if you think about it.

Qualified — by virtue of my unpaid summer internship.

Rust — you try spending 30 years in the rain and hot sun.

Salon — just as good as your local Great Clips and only 4x the price.

Tapas — ok... but where's the rest of the food?

Undertow — Hell, I can't swim in *normal* conditions.

Van — 47 square feet of old socks and open road.

Whoopsie — when you accidentally sit on your pet chinchilla.

Xenobiotic — probably way over prescribed.

Yodeling — thankfully a lost art.

Zipper — the leading cause of scrotum injuries.

*"is it too late to do things the **easy** way??"*

Awkward — making eye contact through that slit in the bathroom stall.

Baldy — my incredibly hurtful nickname.

Cell — do NOT mess with the Mitochondria.

Donkeys — like horses, but without the ego.

Ecstasy — Jesus, I asked if you had Advil, Gary!

Flat — my career trajectory.

Gallstones — an affordable alternative to lumber.

Hillbilly — this truck ain't gonna muddy itself.

Intern — you will sit here from 9 - 5 and pretend to look busy, mister.

Jam — jelly's rich uncle.

Kibbles — a good, wholesome treat for me AND my dog.

Lamb — sick and tired of sheep, I'm sure.

Manager — an inspiring leader and MASSIVE a-hole.

Numbnuts — a long forgotten (and sorely missed) jab from the '90s.

Old — your grandma. (she's 93 for God's sake!)

Poop — what's the occasional bowel movement between friends?

Quit — what I do anytime something gets hard.

Rupture — well that doesn't sound good.

Sarcasm — you probably wouldn't get it.

Toast — I prefer non-crispy bread, thank you.

Urine — looks like lemonade, but certainly doesn't taste like it.

Violence — I said what would happen if you called me, "Thunder Thighs" again.

Warranty — trust me, it's limited.

X-ray — if you wanted to see me naked, all you had to do was ask.

Yoda — shut it, old man!

Zit — the size of a small child, unfortunately.

"home sweet home"

Abs — a reward for being miserable most of the time.

Badminton — nothing like whackin' around a couple of 'cocks in the backyard.

Commandments — Jesus, how many of these things are there?

Dogs — proof that at least *something* likes me.

Europe — come back, England. we're sorry!

Figs — the last thing on my mind right now.

Gag — my bullsh*t is tough to swallow.

Hipsters — is this steak vegan?

Injection — almost always in a butt cheek.

Jury — did he do it? Maybe. Do I need a lunch break? Yes.

Keg — who's the sick f*ck who ordered a Yuengling keg?!

Lethal — farting in the shower.

Mutt — "he's a doodle mix."

EUROPE
(I MEAN, BASICALLY)

Nixon — not a crook, he promises.

Oar — could become a paddle one day if it works hard and believes in itself.

Pinocchio — probably suffered from a serious mental condition.

Quarterback — mom never let me play football :(

Rapper — the #1 profession amongst suburban white kids.

Safety — why I hesitate before sticking my hand down the garbage disposal.

Taxidermy — an incredible way to remember Mr. Barky.

Utter — not sure what else I'd be suckin' on.

Venice — not the ideal location for my new car dealership.

Walmart — a breeding ground for $2 sausage links and scalding hot political takes.

Xi'an — the Chinese sure can name a city.

Yeehaw — I'm screaming on the inside.

Zoom — oh, I can hear you, I just don't care.

"milk this, b*tch!"

Adult — when you use a $10 gift card to buy an oven mitt from Kohl's.

Broccoli — easily my favorite coli.

Creativity — I can't think of a damn thing to put here.

Deaf — I can't hear you, but I don't like your attitude.

Erection — surprisingly common in Europe.

Fern — I killed that, too.

Glacier — not in this climate!

Hotcakes — what old people call pancakes.

Inmate — this shank won't make itself.

Jocks — most certainly still living at home.

Kentucky — has some redeeming qualities, I'm sure.

Lacy — my hairdresser's name.

Maid — if you have to ask, you can't afford one.

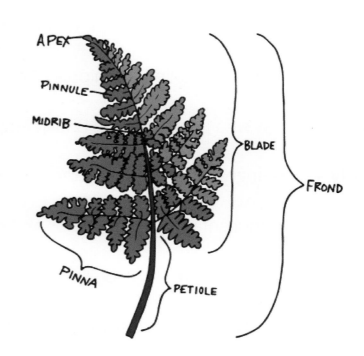

APEX
PINNULE
MIDRIB
BLADE
FROND
PINNA
PETIOLE

Google

🔍 discount maids ✕ 🎤

Nasty — Motel 8's pool after a swinger's convention.

Oil — sure the Arctic's melting, but we have $1.99 gas!

Pancakes — my dad called 'em nipple cakes.

Queen — just who IS running the British empire these days?

Rally — this angry mob won't organize themselves.

Suspect — innocent until proven guil... ok, he did it.

Tall — to my doctors, I'm 5'10. on Hinge, I'm 6'1.

Utah — home to world-class skiing and a heck of a lot of white people.

this bruh short

Visa — couldn't get an AMEX, huh?

Water — bland, boring, essential to life.

X-cuse me — not sure how I managed to sneak this into the X's.

Yellow — I don't floss, ok?!

'Za — what intolerable d-bags call pizza.

"where's your precious hide-a-key now, Gary?"

Aspirations — flew out the window with my 11th kid.

Banana — it's that shape for a reason, folks.

Career — 3 more summers and I'll be Dairy Queen's newest assistant manager.

Deal — these adult diapers won't sell themselves.

Electricity — if you can feel it in the air, RUN!

Faith — apparently held in equal accord to family and football.

Gin — could do so much better than tonic.

Hot — I prefer sexy or cute, pervert.

Indiana — well it's no Illinois, but it'll have to do.

JIF — strangely NOT produced in a factory that handles peanuts.

Kellogg's — Frosted Flakes f*ck.

Laid — abstinent for 6 years now. (3 by choice!)

Mom — the only person who's both wiped AND kicked my ass.

Naive — women find me TOO attractive, that's the problem.

Oreo — part of a balanced breakfast according to TV commercials from the '90s.

Pub — packed with bald Englishmen.

Quack — I've had it up to here with you, duck.

Round — golf balls, oranges, and my big ole booty.

Saggy — my tits didn't always look like this, you know?

Tacos — what I end up making for dinner 5 nights a week.

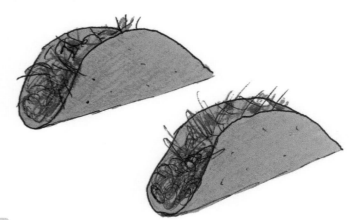

Uruguay — good at soccer, I think.

Vail — good skiing, GREAT cardiologists.

Wave — well I'll be, it's Lieutenant Dan!

Xenopus — probably has like 12 tentacles.

Yard — home to more weeds than a Snoop Dogg BBQ.

Zoo — not sure how we slipped these past the animal rights activists.

"modern romance"

Advice — offered exclusively by the lady cutting your hair at Great Clips.

Books — like Twitter, but longer, on paper, and far less opinionated.

Cholesterol — don't worry, it's the good kind.

Dad — probably on the toilet right now.

Eyebrows — yeah, I pluck 'em. Sue me.

Fishing — are we having fun yet?

Government — what could go wrong?

Halloween — when I head to the basement and pretend like I'm not home.

Invitation — you can come too, I guess.

Jacuzzi — where finding a used Band-Aid is the LEAST of your concerns.

King — you think I wear this crown for fun?

Low — pooping your brains out before realizing there's no toilet paper.

Magic — how I lost my 2nd wife.

Nudes — in the right light, anything looks good.

Oops — whipping out your wee wee on a Zoom call.

Pencil — absolutely useless after you leave high school.

Question — not in my classroom, buster.

Relative — you're not THAT ugly.

Salesman — responsible for 90% of short sleeve button-up sales.

Taboo — farting on an airplane.

Ultrasound — oh, I'm not pregnant, just insanely fat.

Vespa — what I ride when my Harley's in the shop.

Whip — I'm not usually into roleplay, but ok.

Xenogamy — sorry, sweetheart, I'm a married man.

Yo — an incredibly unprofessional way to begin a job interview.

Zillionaire — whoever bought Internet.com.

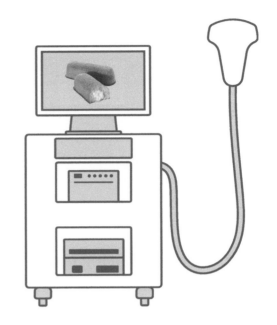

GRAVY

"drawing is to scale"

Accident — you being born... OHHHHH!

Banger — the act of British people sticking their sausage in a hole.

Casino — you've taken everything from me.

Divorce — let's be honest, I was only in it for the money.

Evil — taking the last potato skin at TGI Friday's.

Firemen — that pole ain't for what you think it's for.

Gutsy — sending that, "you up?" text at 7 pm after 6+ hours of day drinking.

Hooters — come for the boobs, stay for the... well, boobs.

Illness — I knew that goat cheese smelled funny.

Jargon — well that's what we call it in the biz, anyway.

Kangaroo — Australian horses.

Lab — these STDs won't test themselves, Barry.

Map — huh, well according to this, we took a wrong turn 12 hours ago.

Nerd — a seemingly surefire way to become rich.

Odor — I sh*t my pants, ok? Is that what you wanted to hear?!

Panda — can hardly call itself a bear.

Questionable — gas station sushi.

Reliable — we all have that one friend who lets us down no matter what.

Soy — for the love of God, please be low sodium.

Tomato — fruit? veggie? who the f*ck cares.

Union — the only reason I get Earth Day off.

Virgin — the best 37 years of my life.

Wax — do NOT tell your barber that you'd like a "Brazilian."

Xebec — no, no, no, you mean *Que*bec.

Yeast — please be the bread kind.

Zaxby's — 5,000 calories in one sitting? Sure, why not?

"be grateful for the 'hoe you have"

Avocado — **insert millennial joke here**

Brothel — look, lady, I'm just here for the salad bar.

Crabapple — always in a terrible mood.

Delivery — it's either that or DiGiorno's.

Emotions — often wildly out of control.

Fate — I truly believe that I was always destined to be a failure.

Garden — that's what grocery stores are for, moron!

Hair — slowly, but surely leaving me.

Interview — 60-90 minutes of wet handshakes and fake laughs.

Jogging — like sprinting, but for fat people.

Kindergarten — where sh*tting your pants isn't just acceptable, it's encouraged!

Lard — surprisingly good in moderation.

Molecule — throw a couple together and you've got yourself a covalent bond, mister.

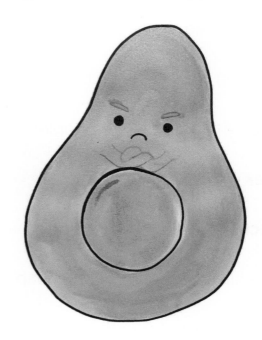

Navy — the Army needs more submarines, I've said it for years.

Ox — when your former wife is too large to be considered just an ex.

Parade — look, old white people!

Quaker — doesn't own a microwave, but always clamoring for the latest iPhone.

Respect — holding the door open with your foot.

Sack — filled with potatoes, probably.

Teeth — just what ARE the British thinking.

Uber — I'll tip you, ok, just don't talk to me.

Vape — big tobacco always finds a way back.

Westminster — so much more than a dog show. (not really.)

Xylocarp — sounds like a severely deformed fish.

Yoga — welp, there goes my hamstring.

'Zona — home to more goatees per square mile than anywhere on earth.

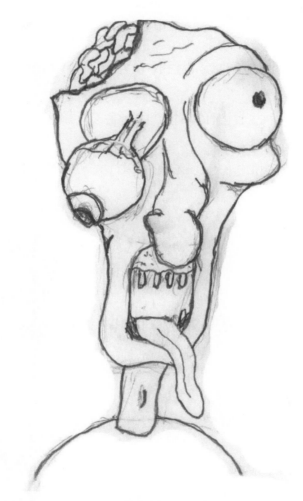

"you should see the other guy"

Attic — just what *is* grandma keeping up there.

Bamboo — Asian lumber.

Candle — the perfect way to tell your mom, "we really aren't that close, are we?"

Drugs — don't worry, officer, I have a prescription for these.

Enlightenment — the moment you realize, and accept, that you're ugly.

Fraternity — sup bro, nice Bean Boots.

Graffiti — yup, that's a penis.

Hush — a very demeaning way to tell someone to be quiet.

Indians — our bad.

Jet — the armrest battle: subtle yet devastating.

Kiwi — the one fruit nobody thinks about.

Lame — exercising and eating right.

McDonald's — should really invest in a mechanic for their ice cream machine.

Nagger — "would it kill you to actually *flush* the toilet when you're done, Derek?"

Oblong — a circle that just couldn't take it anymore.

Porn — I have a problem.

Quality — started low and getting lower.

Rodeo — home to endless steer wrestling and deep fried EVERYTHING.

Seat — airlines must think my a** is 2 inches wide.

Toppings — what the hell happened to TCBY?

Understatement — things could be going better financially.

Vacation — 5 days a year + federal holidays!

Wet — the crucial difference between water-resistant and waterproof.

Xiphoids — like I said, I have a prescription.

Youth — comes *just* before years of endless despair.

Zillow — 3 bedrooms, 2.5 baths, and a lifetime of crippling debt.

"my moccasins!"

Anchovies — the worst aspects of pizza and sushi rolled into one.

Baby — seated directly behind me on this flight.

Concierge — Show me the best Thai place in Boston, stat!

Dairy — why I've been in the bathroom for the last 4 hours.

Encyclopedias — wildly out of date by now.

Flavor — I've sacrificed many a taste bud for hot soup.

Gutter — get your mind out of it, young man.

Hookah — so people know for sure that you're a d-bag.

Instagram — I always assumed that my ex was over me, but it's nice to know for sure.

Jamaica — give it a rest, Sandals. I'm not coming to your sh*tty resort.

Karaoke — just not the same without a microphone.

Lava — should really think about hiring a PR agency.

Mayonnaise — most definitely an instrument.

Neighbor — seems to only borrow my leaf blower when my wife's home alone.

Office — physically, I'm here. Mentally, I'm dead inside.

Pancetta — bacon for rich people.

Quick — hide the milk, mom's lactose!

Rabies — I told you that raccoon didn't look right.

Sabbath — every day if you're lazy.

Talented — that kid in 2nd grade who could burp the ABC's.

Ugly — why 42% of us are desperately alone.

Vengeance — something I wish on no one. (except of course you, Susan.)

Whopper — was McDonald's closed or something?

Xanathan — one of the most popular baby names of 2034.

Yin — yang's around here somewhere.

Zap — Tesla should get into electric fly swatters.

HELLO
my name is

XANATHAN

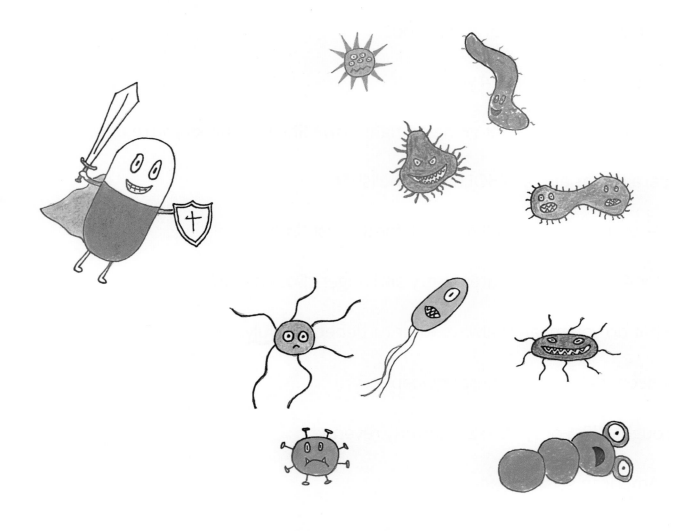

"f*ck you, germs!"

Asbestos — why you or a loved one suffer from Mesothelioma.

Bay — incredibly jealous of inlets and sounds.

Hole		1	2	3	4	5	6	7	8	9	Out
Blue	70.4/114	522	132	397	365	391	513	438	190	402	3350
White	M: 68.7/110 L: 73.6/110	500	117	384	339	365	489	406	160	349	3109
Gold		432	109	334	303	314	449	354	140	327	2762
Red	69.4/110	427	109	290	298	304	449	306	140	325	2648
Lion Trees		4	3	4	4	3	4	4	3	4	33
Me		8	7	7	9	9	12	X	X	X	D.N.F.

Cricket — we started this game 4 years ago.

Dating — she doesn't have, "a lot going on right now." She just thinks you're ugly.

Essay — 5 paragraphs and a WHOLE lot of bullsh*t.

Friendship — you've failed to call me back for the last time.

Golf — $75 for 4 hours of absolute misery and anger? Sounds fun.

Hickey — what do you mean? I always wear turtlenecks in July.

Icicle — the seemingly perfect murder weapon.

Jerseys — roughly 70% of TJ Maxx's quarterly revenue.

Ketchup — American salsa.

Labor — in this economy?!

Mars — I prefer Snickers, but sure it'll do.

Nod — my reaction when anyone asks if I could use a snack.

Outside — not today, nature.

Panic — trust me, you left the oven on.

Quote — I better not see this in tomorrow's paper.

Rough — my privileged upbringing.

Sod — when you're too damn rich to wait for grass seed.

Test — when your wife asks which one of her friends you think is the hottest.

Ukulele — almost always accompanied by a Fedora.

Vampires — have really put a dent in garlic sales.

Wash — your butt must be cleaned AT LEAST twice a week according to the CDC.

Xyster — oyster's 2nd cousin that got shipped off to boarding school.

Yawn — holy sh*t this book is boring.

Zen — the drunken hours between 1 pm - 4 pm.

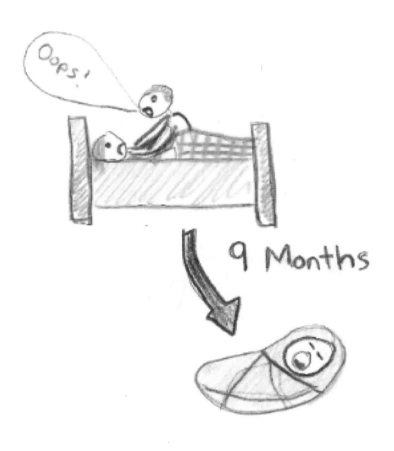

"the miracle of life"

Anticipation — it's just killing me.

Bagels — New Yorkers just won't SHUT UP about them, will they?

Cupboard — home to 453 tupperware lids and 7 bottoms.

Debt — just give me a few decades, I'll be completely out from under this.

Erosion — just where *is* that soil off to now!

Fabric — soft, yet supportive. Like a teddy bear with a rod through its spine.

Gravy — almost certainly one of the 5 major food groups.

Haddock — exclusively served at really, really sh*tty weddings.

Investment — don't worry, I have 1/10th of a Bitcoin.

Jackhammering — now that's between me and the Mrs.

Kinky — I'm not comfortable with any of this.

Lobster — God knows you can't afford market price.

Mole — large, misshapen, strangely comforting.

Necessary — seeing what my poop looks like after I'm done wiping.

Oatmeal — just a terrible, terrible breakfast food.

Prawn — nope, that's a lobster.

Quilt — yet another thing grandma has and I want.

Retire — my financial advisor says I'm on track for 2095.

Stain — seemingly destined for all my white shirts.

Technology — take me back to the days of Myspace and flip phones.

Urban — anywhere with more than one Arby's per square mile.

Velcro — easily a top-5 Invention of 1952.

Warm — wait, you mean that $17 sleeping bag from Walmart *didn't* do the job?

Xylophonist — Verizon's newest job posting.

Yacht — what your cousin calls his 12-year-old pontoon boat.

Zambia — home to the world's largest waterfall. (I'm out of jokes, ok?)

"ouch"

Affect — or is it effect?

Butthole — God DAMN this book is vulgar.

Caesar — made one hell of a salad, apparently.

Disguise — I've always had this mustache.

Excuse — I'd have been here on time, but I don't give a sh*t about you.

Foliage — an incredibly pretentious name for leaves.

Gang — not even they wanted me :(

HBO — a single paid account supplies 90% of U.S. households.

Indifference — me: "I love you." her: "k."

Jorts — these calves aren't gonna tan themselves.

Kale — no.

Lie — you're a strong, beautiful person.

Mechanic — "ok, so while I was fixing your flat tire, your engine exploded."

Nutella — how I got these fantastic love handles.

Orville — a truly, truly terrible name for a baby.

Penis — there's more where that came from! (not really.)

Quid — money for British people, I guess.

Reef — f*ck, we destroyed that, too.

Saloon — 1 part alcohol, 2 parts cowboy hats.

Tits — these bad boys cost more than your car.

Understanding — you just don't GET IT, do you?

Vaseline — solely used to soothe my chapped hiney.

Weapon — a rubber band. (if used correctly.)

X-factor — it's the chili powder.

Yolked — every bald guy at my gym.

Zebra — we all knew this one was coming.

"quiet, please"

Adoption — well you were bound to find out eventually.

Bras — should be supportive and comforting. Just like my ex... please come back.

Cyclist — hit me, I dare ya.

Death — trust me, friend, I died a long time ago.

Emergency — when you've got a pair of smeared cheeks and there's no TP.

Fedora — take it easy, Bruno Mars.

Gastronomy — you don't wanna look up this butt, pal.

Hallmark — dammit do they make a good original movie.

Idiot — the moron demanding to speak with my manager.

Job — I mean I'm sure you enjoyed it at some point, right?

Kids — the only ones brave enough to tell me when my fly is down.

Lean — last seen 40 pounds ago.

Mentor — always told me to follow my dreams. Or, failing that, to get very rich.

Nips — these puppies could pierce the Earth's crust if necessary.

Orgasm — well, *I* certainly enjoyed myself.

Pension — why we need a UNION, dammit!

Queasy — that beef tartare just ain't sittin' right.

Russia — just chill out, will ya?

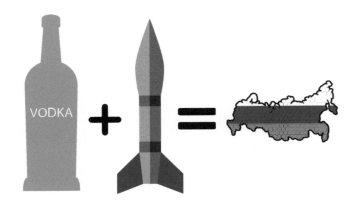

Sister — a younger, far more vengeful version of my mother.

Testosterone — keeping hole-in-wall repairmen in business since 1904.

Uranus — oh, grow up!

Vibe — nothing beats a bar without doors on the bathroom stalls.

Waiter — what can I get you guys to drink?

Xylidine — when regular iodine just won't cut it.

Yahoo — the official email service provider for anyone born before 1930.

Zombie — I mean could things really get worse than they are now?

"amen"

Avalanche — the leading cause of death amongst East Coast elites.

Boobs — oh they're real, buddy.

Cents — just a few more of these pennies, and you'll have yourself a dollar, son.

Destiny — how I came to spend the last 6 hours in this Golden Corral.

Euphoria — that morning pee, baby.

Flint — Jesus, didn't anybody bring a lighter?

Grant — hey, that's my name!

Heaven — send me a postcard.

Inning — holy sh*t, how many of these things are there?

Jest — just say "joke" fancy pants.

Karma — the ONLY reason I'm holding the door open for you.

Lawn — this well-manicured sod won't bring your ex-wife back now will it, Ed?

Mississippi — the universal measurement of one second.

Napkin — TP for your face.

Orgy — this delivery man just won't leave.

Paparazzi — my eyes are up here, perverts.

Quail — the only reason rich people wear boots.

Road — long, dusty, and riddled with Long John Silvers.

Sex — it's been a while.

Telephone — a friendly reminder that your voice inbox has been full since last May.

Ulcer — I knew I shouldn't have eaten those jalapeños.

Vaccine — Don't worry, Karen definitely got hers. **wink, wink**

Wood — just say the word and I'll start choppin'.

Xystos — one of the many Greek gods, I'm sure.

Yancy — the surname of roughly 70% of soybean farmers.

Zesty — anything but missionary.

"jerk from home"

Assault — when you slap the sh*t out of somebody givin' you lip.

Brewery — nothing says fun like drinking around children.

Centimeter — just say inch, Frenchy.

Devil — the force behind that 3 am drunk text.

Employee — complaining that you don't make enough while doing the absolute bare minimum.

Fair — look, you may need an excuse to eat fried candy, but I don't.

Gel — my name is Gil, a**hole.

Hello — the ideal greeting when someone walks in on you in the bathroom.

Impregnate — I made a whoopsie.

Jupiter — has always been jealous of Saturn's rings.

Katrina — too soon.

Liverwurst — just as bad as it sounds.

Masturbation — I was just taking a long shower.

Narcissist — you know it, I know it — I'm f*cking awesome.

Obituary — "survived by her only son, Mark, whom she hated."

Pimple — 33 is a hard age.

Quadriceps — the ladies go crazy over a nicely chiseled pair of hammys.

Rye — undoubtedly the worst kind of bread.

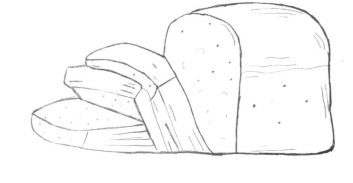

Sand — the only surface hotter than the sun.

Toronto — it's the 'Leafs year, baby.

Unbelievable — the fact that you paid money for this book.

Valuables — you know it's bad when Play It Again Sports won't take your crap.

Wave — uh, I was looking at the person behind you.

Xylol — it's really not that funny.

Yuan — the man she left me for.

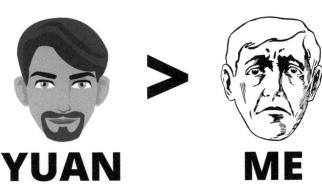

YUAN > **ME**

Zuppa — what your Long Island family calls dinner.

Europe

PORTSMOUTH

"close enough"

Audit — fine, I don't have 12 dependents, so what?

Barber — has a *very* loose definition of, "take a little off the top."

Concussion — f*ck, it's bright out here.

Dentists — seemingly obsessed with my lack of flossing.

Endurance — 15, 20 seconds? Not baddddddd.

Flute — a vastly underutilized wind instrument.

Gazelle — have they tried asking the lions nicely to stop eating them?

Honeymoon — the beginning of a long, happy marriage. (12% of the time.)

Igloo — a relative boom or bust industry in southern Florida.

Jockey — what they lack in size they make up for in Mint Juleps.

Kelly — my middle name. (Do NOT double check that.)

Lesson — when it comes to toilet paper, you get what you pay for.

Mushroom — a truly ABYSMAL pizza topping. "But I like mushrooms!" Shut up.

Naked — the best way to experience a nice, cool summer breeze.

Oarlocks — sounds like a dope new hairstyle.

Pickle — could've been a cucumber with the right education.

Quiz — I'm sure the teacher will round your 47% up to an A.

Redo — it's high time for Home Alone 5.

Scarecrows — have shown a shocking lack of motivation lately.

Tempting — a buffet dumpling that I've just dropped on the floor.

Umbellet — is a word, apparently.

Venison — I'm sorry, but these baby cows are delicious.

Waffles — imagine the breakfast monopoly if IHOP and Waffle House merged.

Xenobiotic — damn you, Purdue Pharmaaaaaaaaa!!!!!

Yearbook — absolutely crawling with penises.

Zinco — Spanish for 50.

Age — just a number. unless they're under 18, then you have yourself a felony.

Baler — we lost a lot of good arms in there.

Computers — eh, probably just a fad.

Democracy — oh, stick to sports!

Exercise — squatting over a public toilet.

Facebook — it's always somebody's damn birthday, isn't it?

Gyro — I know that's not how you say it, just give me some f*ckin' food!

Hoe — what I call my garden tools when they're behaving badly.

Ignorant — I haven't read a book since 2004.

Jacksonville — ahhhh, the Big Apple.

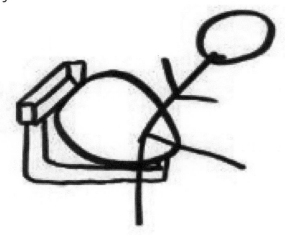

Keys — I don't know what 90% of these open.

Lettuce — a waste of my chewing power.

Mustard — how I'm spicing up my current relationship.

Nectarine — talk dirty to me, you tiny little orange.

Obligated — to see my sh*thead nephew whenever he's in town.

Puppy — poop is everywhere and I haven't slept in 4 days.

Quebec — probably just beautiful this time of year.

Raft — how I'm getting off this damn island.

Society — why I sleep with one eye open.

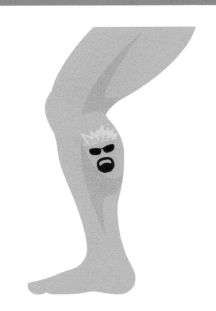

Tattoo — of course that's Guy Fieri's face.

Uh-oh — I'm pregnant.

Vegas — a nice, relaxing weekend unlike any other.

Wagon — I'd have preferred a car for my 16th birthday, but thanks anyway, Mom.

Xenograft — sounds painful.

Yegg — sounds like the name of a genetically modified egg start-up.

Zone — the law forbids me from being this close to a school.

"I'm a grower, I swear!"

Airport — an $18 sandwich? Why the hell not.

Bravery — "of course you look fat in that dress, honey. you're morbidly obese!"

Cop — the light was yellow, I swear!

Diarrhea — beginning to wonder if that curry was worth it.

Envelopes — how many tongues will they mangle before something is done?

Fragment — nope, this here is a sentence.

Guys — ALWAYS have their hands down their pants.

Hybrid — 50% gas, 50% electric, 100% out of my budget.

Impatient — I ordered this Happy Meal well over 90 seconds ago.

June — let's be honest, it's no July.

Keep — those old baseball cards, Mom!

Limes — will never be lemons no matter how hard they try.

Motivation — it was all I could do to put pants on this morning.

Nashville — likes their women country and their chicken hot.

Obese — one day I hope to just be fat.

Pillow — filled with my hopes, dreams, and a significant amount of goose down.

Quesadilla — 15% meat, 85% "other" at Taco Bell.

Roast — seemingly the only way to cook a duck.

Satan — my 8th grade English teacher.

Tan — I haven't seen the sun in days.

Uncle — the ideal mix of love, support, and creepiness.

Venom — which one of you put a rattle on this harmless garden snake?

Why — is printer ink so God damn expensive?

Xenophobia — BUILD. THAT. MALL. (I love Forever 21.)

Yearly — how often I'm content.

Zinger — your father-in-law's joke about the liberal who walked into a bar.

5 out of 4
People Do Not
Understand Fraction
Jokes

Antibiotics — take 3 every 8 hours for that javelin sticking out of your chest.

Backhoe — one of Susan's many nicknames.

Card — what can this $6 Hallmark say that my folded computer paper can't?

Dizzy — no concussed, I'm not coach.

Euphemism — I'm insanely horny. (If you know what I mean.)

Friends — anybody I feel comfortable farting in front of.

Germs — that final .01% just won't die.

Herpes — nah, it's just a few cold sores.

Identity — I lost mine a long, long time ago.

Jerk — both a Caribbean seasoning and anyone named Anthony.

Keto — Dr. Adkins after a few cosmetic surgeries.

Laundry — the worst part of the year.

Mystery — where 99% of my socks end up.

Nun — avert your eyes, sister.

Obscene — holster that middle finger, bucko.

Pest — Sorry, Terminix said nothing could be done about your mother-in-law.

Quarrel — how 16th century Europe worked sh*t out.

Radish — a nice, wholesome dessert.

Sad — dropping your takeout while getting out of the car.

Tuna — more expensive per pound than my home.

Underwater — I was wondering why it was so hard to breathe.

Vacuum — the most evil thing ever, according to my dog.

Willow — if it ain't weepin', it's not for me.

Xerox — I need 37 copies of my hiney, stat.

Yelp — 1-star for using small menu font.

Zero — my approximate net worth.

Personal accounts

Adv Plus Banking	$0.13
Regular Savings	-$11.90
Bank of America Cash Rewards Visa Signature	$47,566.04

"dealer's choice"

Allergies — what your co-worker says she has before giving you Smallpox.

Bonfire — gonna have to downgrade this to a regular fire if it gets any smaller.

Complacency — sets in about 2 weeks into any job.

Data — I don't need your fancy "numbers" to tell me that I'm overweight, ok?!

Election — currently waitlisted at the Electoral College.

Framed — we can admit it now, OJ did it.

Gulls — plotting to steal my french fries as we speak.

Hoop — like you, I was the LeBron James of 3rd grade rec basketball.

Incest — well, if you insist.

Joe — the guy at work you say hi to in the hallway, but *never* in the bathroom.

Korea — where getting lost around the border is a VERY big deal.

Lust — no, wanting to spank me doesn't count.

Mansion — any home with 2 or more bathrooms.

Nothing — what I have left after investing my life savings in GameStop shares.

Ounce — just didn't have what it took to become a gram or pound.

Pale — it's the SPF 100 that's the problem.

Questionnaire — how I found my 2nd wife.

Red — my face after "accidentally" farting at work.

Solitude — an extrovert's nightmare.

Toboggan — a relic of another era... like non-stretchy pants.

University — a place of higher learning and unlimited dining hall swipes.

Vision — 20/20, no big deal.

Wallet — holds my cash, cards, and an unused condom from 7 long years ago.

Xanthone — an organic compound. (that one's true.)

Yarn — an EXCELLENT birthday present for someone you hate.

Zinc — absolutely delicious when sprinkled on eggs.

"maybe it's jelly?"

Ass — 2 mostly symmetrical cheeks that get a little bigger every year.

Butcher — the guy who hands me boneless, skinless chicken breasts.

Caddy — gimmie a pitching wedge. "But you're 300 yards out?" YOU HEARD ME!

Dictator — you're free to vote for anybody... so long as that person is me.

Ex-girlfriend — I HATE YOU! Also, are you free later? I'd like to talk.

Formula — if it's not quadratic, it's not for me.

German — we get it, you like beer.

Height — as long as you're over 6'4, girls couldn't care less.

Island — coconuts should 100% taste like chocolate instead.

Justified — he did tell you what would happen if you said that again.

Kitten — cute, cuddly, deadly.

Laughter — a shockingly ineffective medicine according to the latest clinical trial.

Mature — I'll ALWAYS think farts are funny.

Nachos — my doctor says they're not good for me, but f*ck him.

Osmosis — the only thing any of us remember from high school bio.

Puss — I just threw up in my mouth.

Quarterfinalist — winning is overrated.

Rad — what old dudes call waking up at 6 A.M. for their walk around the block.

Salami — it's not the first time you've put your meat between my buns.

Tupperware — where the HELL are the lids?!

Uggs — the official shoe of highly privileged middle schoolers since 2006.

Vagisil — oh yeah, they sell it in bulk.

Wasteful — throwing away all the healthy food I bought at the store last week.

Xylograph — f*ck geometry.

Yahtzee — WAY more fun than an iPad. (kinda.)

Zumba — if I wanted to watch old ladies dance, I'd go to a nursing home.

"alright, NOW we're alone"

MY PARENTS.

Some may see this final section as a fitting tribute to my loving parents...

They will be wrong.

I decided to bring special attention to them **NOT because I'm a good son.**

But because they amassed a small fortune buying domain names in the '90s.

And I'd like to be left SexToysЯus.com.

MOM.

My mom is the kind of person who always has your back.

She doesn't give a sh*t what anybody thinks.

It's her way or the highway.

I called a kid a "freak" in middle school and his dad wanted me suspended.

When the principal brought up the possibility, my mom told him to, "get real."

That story makes me sound like a bully (I wasn't) and my mom sound like a bada** (she is).

Thanks, Mom.

DAD.

My dad is the kind of person who will make you stop in the middle of nowhere and listen.

"You hear that?" he'll say, "...nothing."

The sound of silence.

Some people go their whole lives without hearing it...

But not him.

And because of him, not me.

Thanks, Dad.

BECCA.

Becca and I met on July 6th, 2019, when my roommates and I hosted a "kegger" in our basement.

But since so many friends were out of town, only 9 people came.

Becca was one of those people.

I still remember the moment she came down the stairs...

My heart literally skipped a beat.

We moved in together in March of 2020.

We didn't know it at the time, but we'd spend the next year stuck at home watching roughly 700 episodes of the British reality show, *Love Island*.

And if fit, chatty Englishmen taught me anything over that time, it's that you should always tell people how you feel.

So, Becca, this is how I feel...

BECCA.

I love you.

I love your heart.

I love that I'm comfortable farting around you.

I love that you love kids.

I love your big smile.

I love making coffee for you in the morning. (Not really.)

I love that you eat more bacon than me.

I love that you cry more for others than for yourself.

I love how you tuck in the couch cushions.

I love when you dance.

I love you... but I don't want to be your boyfriend anymore.

SHE SAID YES!

Well, I'm assuming.

This book went to print before I asked her.

I plan to sit down together and read the entire book from start to finish.

If she didn't claw her eyes out from boredom, she'll have seen this proposal with an actual ring taped to that final drawing.

THAT'S IT.

My life, unlike yours, will be forever shaped by this book.

It's been my dream for a long, long time to be an author.

And while I envisioned selling millions of copies with my first book, 102 Kickstarter backers will forever be how I got my start.

I will write other books.

Likely just as unpolished, crass, and wonderfully stupid as this one.

My next idea is a cookbook titled, "Preheat Your Oven to OH-F*CK!"

Until then — share much, love much, and be brave.

SPECIAL THANKS.

To Patrick for teaching me to stand up for what you believe in — even if you're standing there alone.

To Mom, Dad, and Ryan for pretending like this was a good idea.

To Becca for giving me the courage to keep going when I wanted to quit AND for filming me naked.

(Although she should really be thanking ME for that.)

And to people like you who made this whole thing possible.

ABOUT THE AUTHOR.

Grant Stimmel has a PhD in Linguistic Arts from the University of Oxford.

While there, he specialized in Medieval children's stories about the Bubonic Plague.

(He's also known to fabricate certain details about his life.)

"F" is for Flush is Grant's first book.

If you're lucky, it will be his last.

He lives in Charlotte, North Carolina with his fiancé Becca and their dog Theo.

He hopes to one day make something of himself.